D1541917

COWBOY SAM AND BIG BILL
COWBOY SAM
COWBOY SAM AND FREDDY
COWBOY SAM AND THE RODEO
COWBOY SAM AND THE RUSTLERS

COWBOY SAM AND PORKY
COWBOY SAM AND SHORTY
COWBOY SAM AND THE FAIR
COWBOY SAM AND THE INDIANS

COWBOY SAM AND DANDY
COWBOY SAM AND MISS LILY
COWBOY SAM AND FLOP
COWBOY SAM AND SALLY
COWBOY SAM AND THE AIRPLANE

pictures by Jack Merryweather

Cowboy Sam

by Edna Walker Chandler

BENEFIC PRESS · CHICAGO

PUBLISHING DIVISION OF BECKLEY-CARDY COMPANY

STORIES

Copyright 1978, 1971, 1960 by Benefic Press
All Rights Reserved
Printed in the United States of America

Cowboy Sam on the Ranch

Here is Cowboy Sam.

Here is Dandy.

Dandy is Cowboy Sam's horse.

This is Sam's.

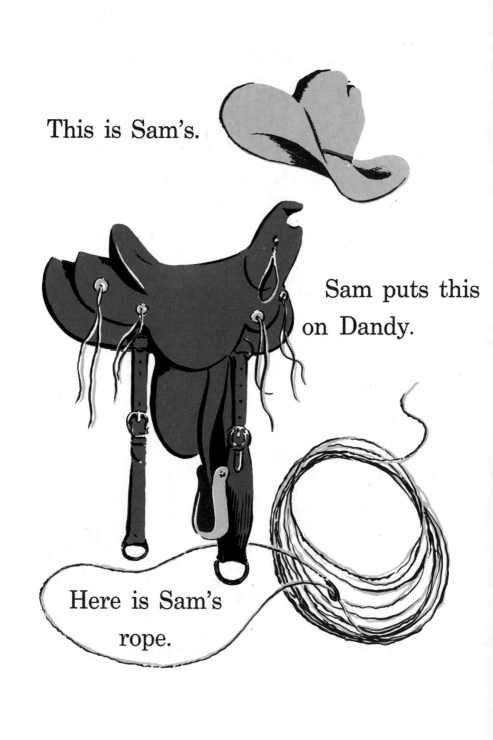

Sam puts this
on Dandy.

Here is Sam's
rope.

Here is Big Bill.
He makes good things
for Sam to eat.

Here is Shorty.

He is a cowboy, too.

He helps Sam.

Here is Sam's ranch.
Sam and Shorty work
on the ranch.
Big Bill works here, too.
They sleep and eat here.

Sam rides with the cows.
He takes the cows away
to get water.
Sam does not have
water at his ranch.

Sam Helps the Little Calf

One day a little calf ran away.
Its mother did not see it.
The little calf wanted
its mother.
Sam saw the little calf.

Sam and Dandy went
after the little calf.
The little calf ran and ran.
Sam used his rope
to stop the calf.

Sam's rope went
over the little calf.
Sam took the little calf.
He took the little calf
to its mother.

"Here is your mother,
little calf," said Sam.
"Now you can eat
your dinner."

The little calf ran to its mother.
It ran to eat its dinner.
"Maaa!" said the little calf.
The little calf liked to eat.

Then the calf went to sleep.

It went to sleep with its mother.

Sam's Work

Sam rode away on Dandy.
He rode with the cows.
He rode and rode.

The sun went down.
Sam took the cows
back to the ranch.

Soon the cows and calves
will sleep.

Dandy's work was over
for the day.

Sam gave Dandy a good dinner.

Sam's work was over for the day.
Big Bill gave Sam his dinner.

Cowboy Sam Looks for Black Wolf

Cowboy Sam was going
to ride his horse, Dandy.

Big Bill saw Sam and Dandy.

"I am going to take the cows
to water," said Sam.

"I will look for Black Wolf."

"Did Black Wolf come?"
asked Bill.

"Did he come in the night?"

"Black Wolf ran after
the cows in the night," said Sam.

"He ran after the little calves.
Black Wolf is bad.
He must not be near the cows."

"Do you want me to ride
with you?" asked Shorty.
"I want you to work
on the ranch," said Sam.
"I will," said Shorty.
"I will do good work here."

"I will come back soon,"
said Cowboy Sam.

"I will want a good dinner."

"Good-by," said Big Bill.

"I will make a good dinner."

"Good-by, Sam," said Shorty.

"Good-by," said Cowboy Sam.

Cowboy Sam rode Dandy.

He rode with the cows.

The cows stopped to eat grass.

They liked grass.

They liked water, too.

The sun went down.
Then it was night.
The cows went to sleep.
"I will eat now,"
said Cowboy Sam.
"Then I will sleep, too."

Cowboy Sam had something to eat.
Cowboy Sam wanted to sleep.
"I will make a big fire,"
he said.
"Black Wolf will not
come near a big fire."

"This is a good fire," said Sam.
Sam put his gun near him.

Black Wolf Comes

Cowboy Sam went to sleep
near the fire.

Then Sam heard something.
The big cows heard something.
The little calves heard it, too.
They said, "Maaa!"

Cowboy Sam looked around.
He took his gun.
He went around the fire.
Sam looked and looked.
Then he saw something.

He saw two big yellow spots.

"It is Black Wolf!" Sam said.
Sam shot at the two spots.
"Bang! Bang!" went the gun.

The yellow spots went away.
"Black Wolf will not
come back," said Cowboy Sam.

The big cows went to sleep.
The little calves went to sleep.
Cowboy Sam went to sleep, too.

Black Wolf
did not come back.

Sam and the Snake Bite Box

Sam was going to take the cows
to get water.

He looked at the sun.

"The sun will be hot," he said.

"The cows must have water
on a hot day," said Shorty.
"Snakes will come out
on a hot day," said Sam.
"Snakes will want water, too.
We must look for snakes."

"You will have to take
the snake bite box," said Shorty.
"I will take it," said Sam.

"Do you want me to work
on the ranch?" said Shorty.
Sam said, "I want you
to ride with me."
"Good!" said Shorty.
"I like to ride."

Sam and Shorty took
the snake bite box.
They took good things to eat.
Big Bill gave Sam and Shorty
good things to eat.

"I will make a good dinner
when you come back," said Bill.

"Good," said Sam.

"We like your dinners."

"Good-by," said Shorty.

"Good-by," said Bill.

Sam and Shorty went
to get the cows.
The cows ran out.

Sam rode Dandy.

Shorty rode Blacky.

They rode away with the cows.

They rode and rode.

They looked for water.

Shorty rode away.

Sam rode with the cows.

Shorty saw water.

There was very little water.

"We must have more water,"
said Shorty.

Sam and the Snakes

Shorty rode back to Sam.

"You ride with the cows," said Sam.

"I will look for water now."

Then Shorty said, "Here is the snake bite box.

You take it with you."

"The snakes have not come out," said Sam.

"But I will take the box."

Sam took the snake bite box.
He rode away on Dandy.
Shorty was with the cows.
Dandy was a good horse.
He helped Sam look
for water.

Then Dandy stopped.

He saw something in the grass.

"Something is in the grass,"
said Sam.

It was a snake Sam saw!
The snake bit Dandy!
Sam took out his gun.
Sam shot the snake.

Sam took the snake bite box.
He helped Dandy's snake bite.
He took Dandy to water.

Sam saw one more snake.
He shot the snake.
Sam did not want a snake
to bite him.

"I must look for snakes,"
said Sam.

"Snakes are bad."

Sam looked and looked.

He did not see more snakes
in the grass.

"I must look for Shorty.
I can not ride Dandy back
to the ranch," said Sam.
"I will come back to you
soon, Dandy.
I can not ride you now!"

Sam saw the cows.

Shorty was with the cows.

"I have water for the cows," said Shorty.

"It is good you had me take the snake bite box," said Sam.

"A snake bit Dandy."

"Will Dandy get well soon?
A snake bite is a bad thing,"
said Shorty.

Sam said, "Dandy will be
well soon."

Two Good Cowboys

"You take the cows and calves
back to the ranch," said Sam.

"They had water.

They had grass.

Dandy and I will stop here.

We will come to the ranch
when Dandy is well."

Shorty said, "I will take
the cows back to the ranch."

"You did good work,"
said Shorty.
"You shot Black Wolf.
You looked for water.
You shot two snakes.
You helped Dandy."

"You helped, too," said Sam.
"You looked for water.
You had me take the
snake bite box."
"I like a cowboy's work,"
said Shorty.

"I like it, too," said Sam.
"But it is too bad
the snake bit Dandy."
"Good-by," said Sam.
"You go back to the ranch.
I will be here with Dandy.
But I will come to the
ranch soon."

Sam went back to Dandy.

Shorty took the cows.

Sam and Shorty were
good cowboys.

They did ranch work well.

VOCABULARY

The total vocabulary of this book is 113 words excluding proper names. Of these, 44 are pre-primer words and are not listed below. Forty-six are primer words and are listed in roman type; 23 are above primer level and appear below in italic type. The number indicates the page on which the word first appears.

after 14
around 34
at 36

back 20
bad 25
be 25
bit 52
bite 40
box 40
but 49

calf 13
cowboy 10
cows 12

day 13
dinner 16
do 26
does 12

eat 9

fire 30

gave 22
get 12
going 24
good-by 27
grass 28
gun 3

had 30
heard 33
helps 10
him 31
his 12
horse 7
hot 40

its 13

make 9
more 48
must 25

near 25
night 25
now 16

out 41
over 15

puts 8

ranch 5
ride 12
rode 19
rope 8

shot 36
sleep 11
snakes 40
something 30
soon 21
spots 35
stopped 14
sun 20

take 12
then 18
there 48
things 9
took 15
two 35

used 14

very 48

was 22
water 12
well 58
when 45
work 11

yellow 35
your 16